THINGS I WANT TO SAY AT WORK BUT CAN'T: TEACHER'S EDITION

J.J. HURLEY

RAINBOW LADA PRESS

FLORIDA, USA

Published by Rainbow Lada Press
An imprint of Rainbow Lada LLC
2462 Laurel Rd E #573
Nokomis, FL 34275 USA
Email: rainbowlada0@gmail.com

First edition: April 2023
ISBN: 979-8-89035-007-7

This book belongs to

Use this page to test colors and check for bleeding.

Tip: if using markers try putting a blank piece of paper or a piece of plastic underneath each page before coloring.

Note: this page is repeated in the back of the book.

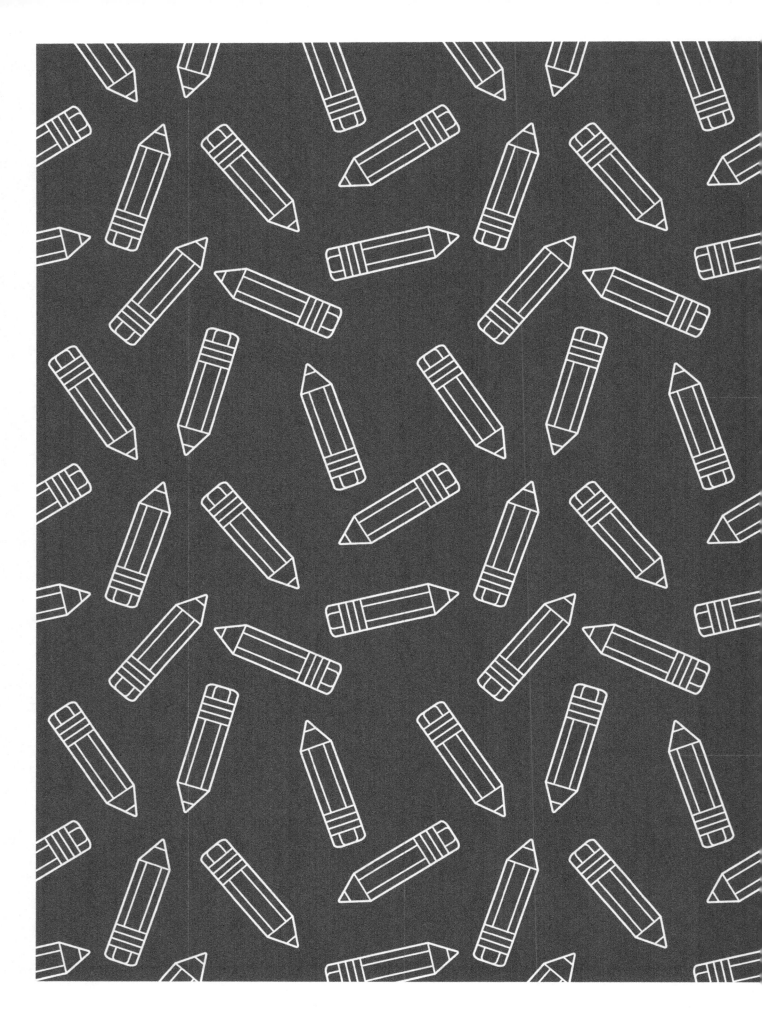

Teaching Is Like

HIKING UP AN ERUPTING VOLCANO

During A Tornado

WHILE BEING CHASED

BY ZOMBIES

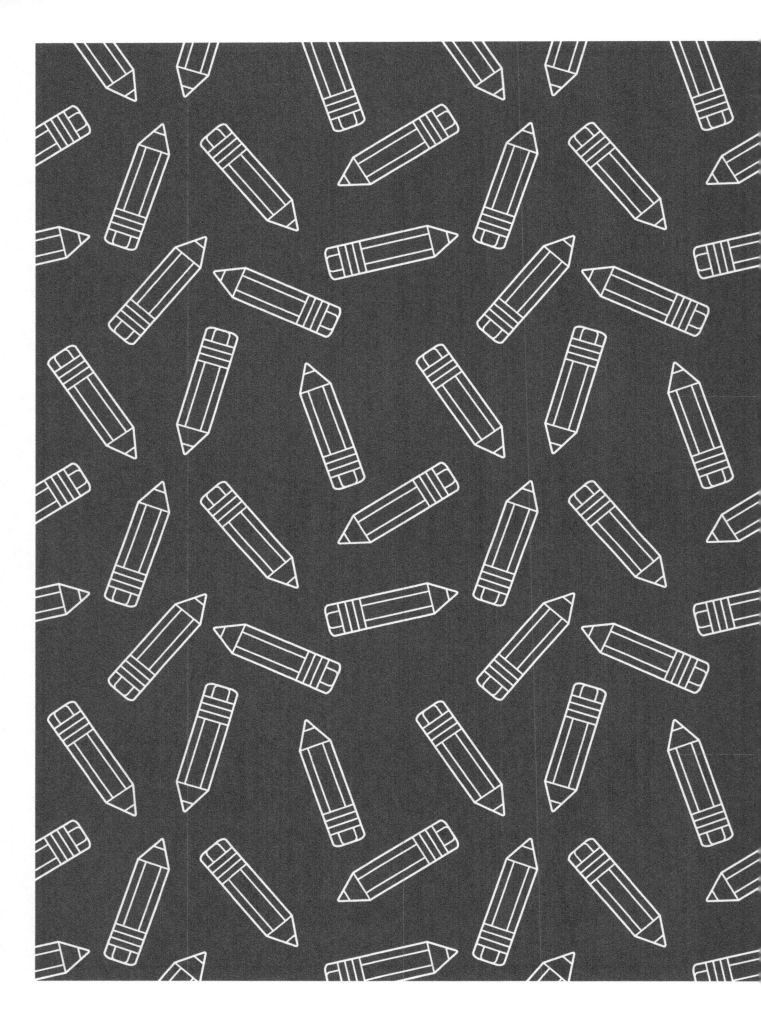

Are You Bleeding?

No?

Dying?

No?

Then Sit Down.

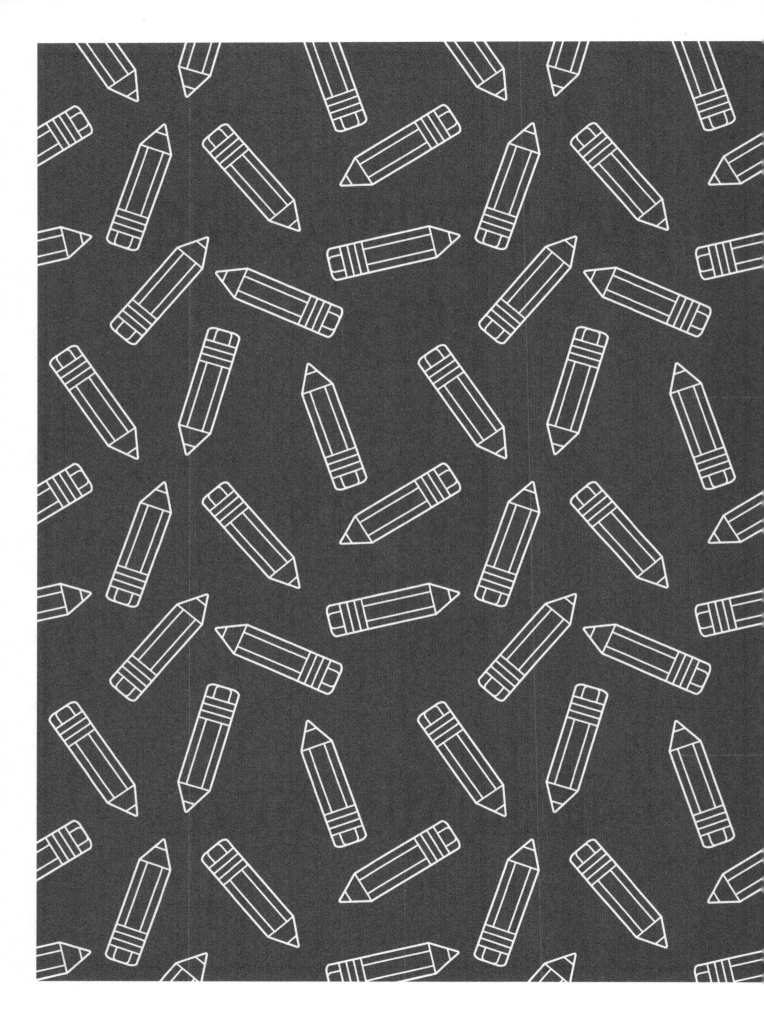

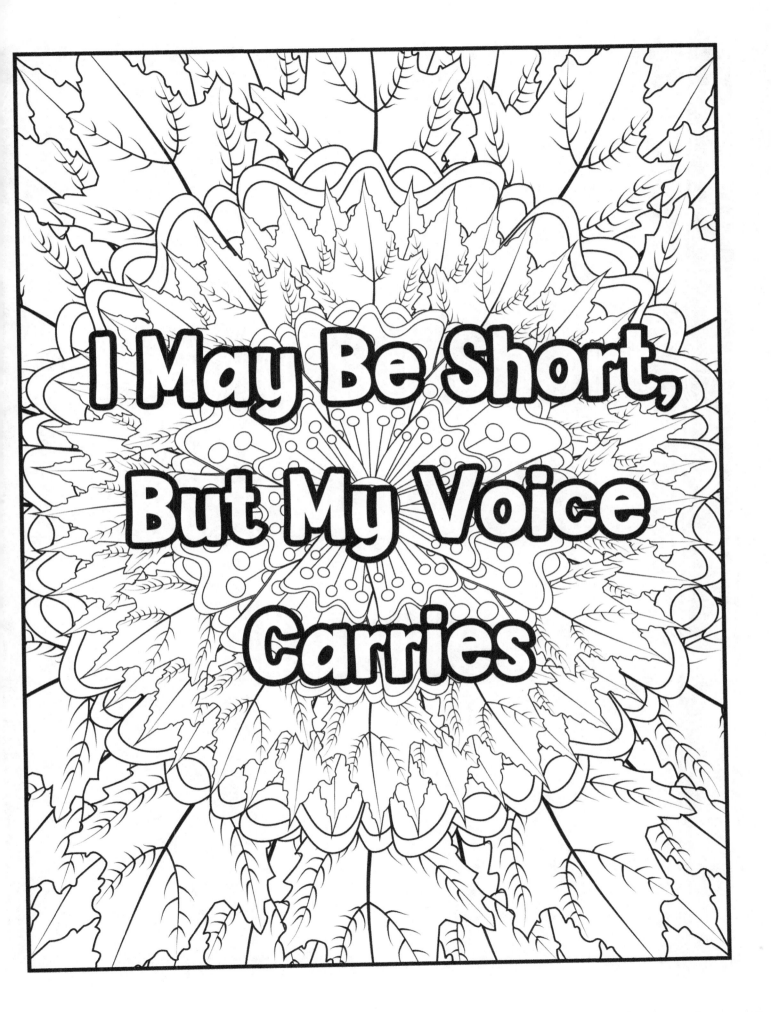

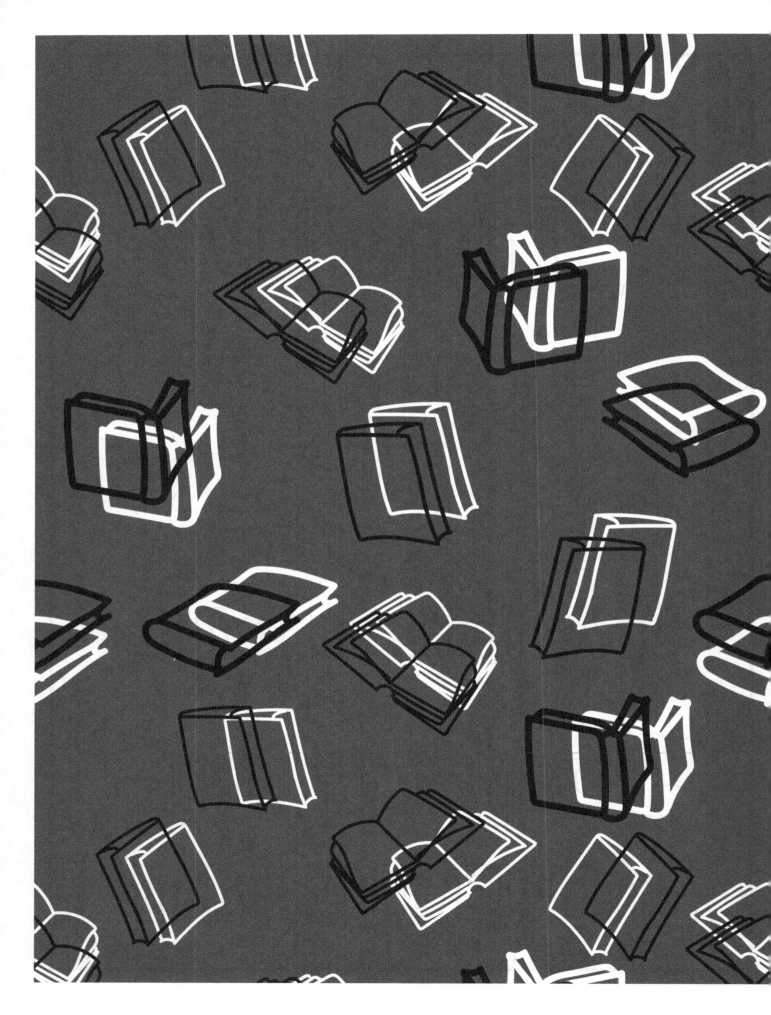

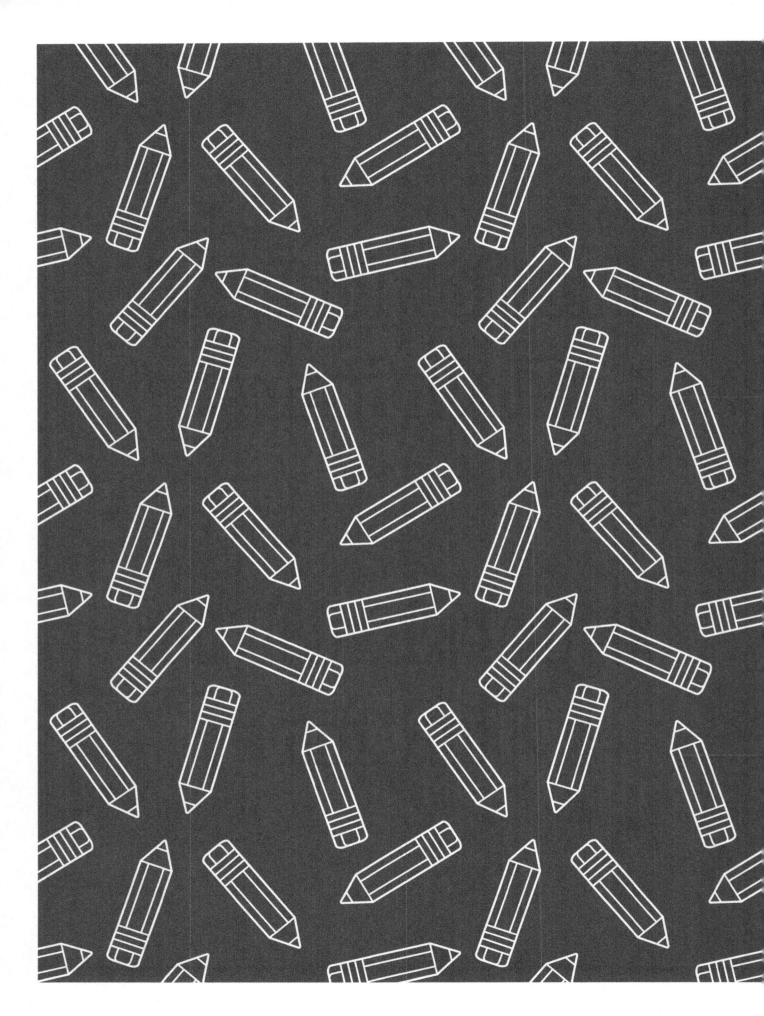

I Love Grading Papers So Much, I Do It In My Sleep

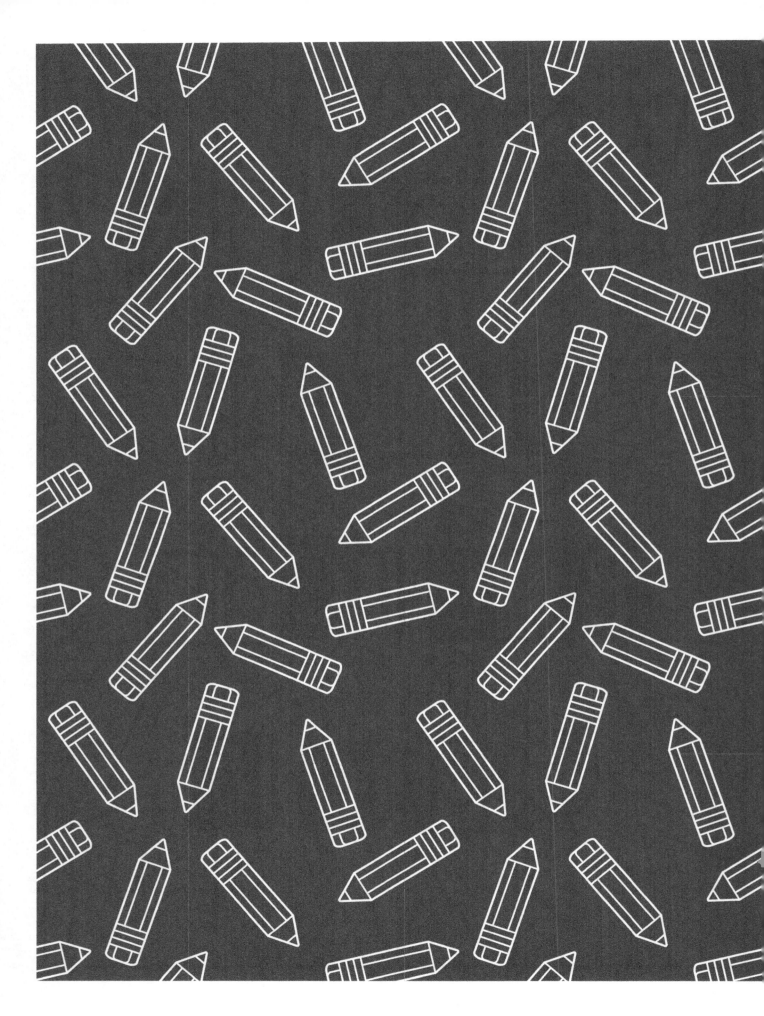

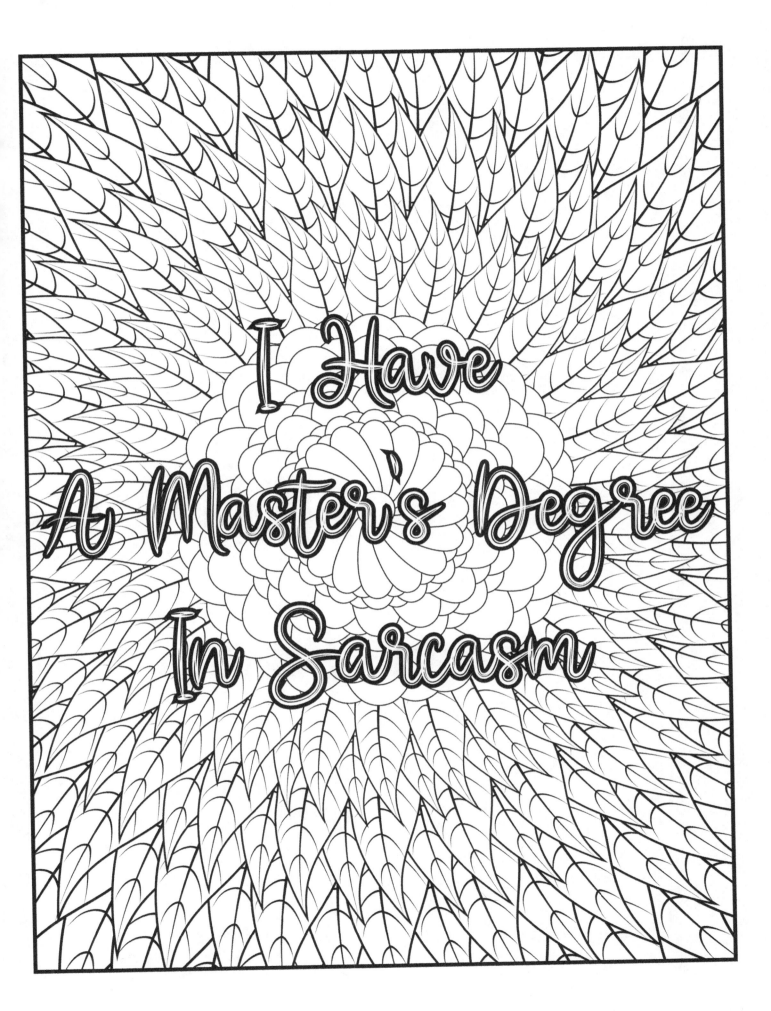

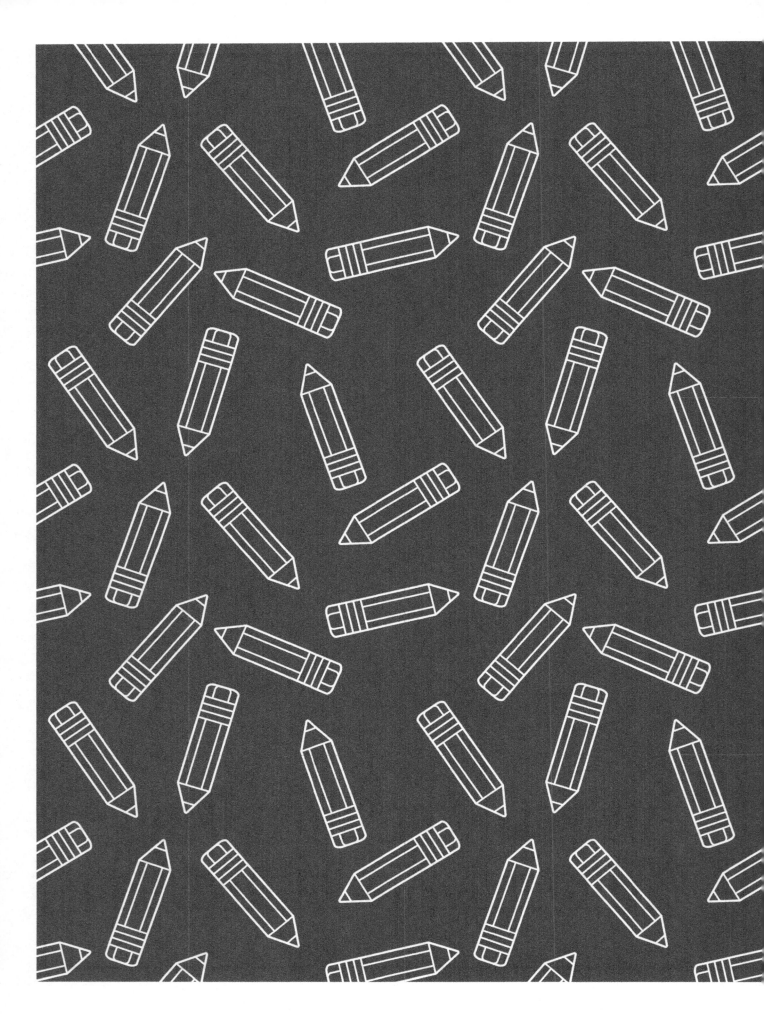

I MAY NOT BE A
Magician
BUT I CAN MAKE 30 KIDS DISAPPEAR FOR AN HOUR

Use this page to test colors and check for bleeding.

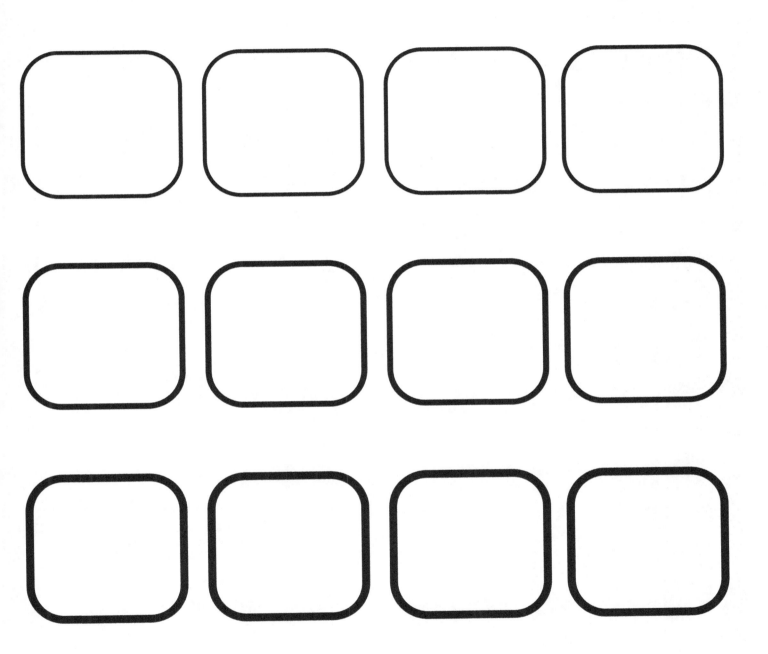

Tip: if using markers try putting a blank piece of paper or a piece of plastic underneath each page before coloring.

Note: this page is repeated in the front of the book.

Rainbow Lada Press is an imprint of Rainbow Lada, LLC.

At Rainbow Lada Press, we publish books that bring joy and laughter to people, regardless of who they are.

https://rainbowladapress.com

Interested in more funny office gifts? Check out the rest of our coloring books, and a line of notebooks with funny sayings on the cover!

Thank you for buying this book. I hope it brought a smile to your day!

J.J. Hurley

Made in the USA
Monee, IL
11 December 2024

73224204R00039